Whether a crisis hits during or after business hours, your staff - and therefore your bottom line - will be affected.

Productivity, morale and relationships at work, at home and on the front-line will suffer. Knowing how to react and respond appropriately everyday, support others and take care of yourself helps everyone survive and flourish, and gets people back to productive work more quickly.

As a human resources professional, manager, CEO, labourer, parent, partner, co-worker or friend, you are first and foremost a human being. If your company's training programs don't include the 'human element', you may be leaving your most valuable asset – your workforce - unprotected. The human component of any management or leadership plan is key for business survival!

This book is designed to motivate you to revisit and evaluate your approach to communicating and helping others through the difficult situations we all experience at one time or another in our personal and professional lives.

This may include a merger, a corporate sale, the death of a loved one or co-worker, a divorce, the loss of financial security, a job change or move, illness, aging, new management at work, or any other crisis situation.

Life Interrupted will visit your sensitive side, work with the emotional side of life and provide you with a deeper understanding of yourself and others – excellent skills for any leader!

"Laurie's honest examples, candor in dealing with sensitive topics, and organized approach make this guide an important asset for companies, Human Resources departments, and individuals."

Sheryl Lubbock
President, TRIMATRIX
Management Consulting Inc

Life
Interrupted

Your Guide –
Understanding
People in Crisis

Laurie M. Martin

This book is published by the author through TRIMATRIX Management Consulting Inc. www.trimatrixconsulting.com

Cover art by: Monika Kessling, Santa Monica, CA
Author photograph by: Todd Hobley, TDH Photography

For information, please contact:
info@lifeinterrupted.ca
www.lifeinterrupted.ca

ISBN: 1-897144-71-7
First edition. Published in Canada.

Library and Archives Canada Cataloguing in Publication

Martin, Laurie M.
        Life interrupted : your guide to understanding people in crisis /
Laurie
M. Martin. -- 1st ed.

Includes index.
ISBN 1-897144-71-7

        1. Crisis intervention (Mental health services). I. Title.

RC480.6.M36 2005   616.89'025   C2005-907440-X

How you will benefit from this book

In this book, you will find valuable reference information and tools that will assist you in handling, as well as preparing in advance for crisis situations. It contains thought-provoking stories and clear guidelines for reflection, learning and planning.

To enhance your learning and gain a better understanding of the material included, we suggest:

* Reading *Life Interrupted* in its entirety.
* Making notes on the pages provided, to record your impressions, thoughts, and insights, which will provide you with a handy reference to key sections as they apply to your business or life.
* Periodically reviewing *Life Interrupted* to reacquaint yourself with key points, your noted thoughts and revisiting the plans you have in place.
* Sharing this book with others who may also benefit from its content.

Life Interrupted describes what it is like when life is going along just fine and suddenly something happens that interrupts its flow.

> When my brother was tragically killed in a snowmobile accident, my husband and I were reminiscing about the good times we had and talking about how sad it will be for our family and my brother's family, and how all of our lives were suddenly interrupted by this sadness. Life was interrupted.

And, I knew at that moment that this phrase was the perfect description for my company and the services 'Life Interrupted Incorporated' provides.

So, remember this book. Don't just leave it to the side and forget about it. There may be a time in your life – perhaps not now – when you will need to take time for yourself and reflect on the information. Share this book with others so that they can also learn about themselves, and understand others in crisis.

If *Life Interrupted* touches your life, please let me know. Your suggestions and comments are most welcome. And, this is the gift you can share with me. Read on and enjoy…

Preface

This book is intended as a guide. It provides many of the best strategies I've learned from personal experience and from others. When it comes to helping yourself or someone else with a crisis, it should not be considered as the only tool. There are many excellent resources available.

This book has been written to open your mind to new learning and shift old learning into new and creative perspectives. It is intended as a guide, to help you understand people in crisis and how you can offer effective support. Hopefully, it will help you realize the strength of the human spirit.

In writing this book, I have drawn on the knowledge, skills and experiences of many people I've had the privilege to walk alongside throughout my life.

I have learned about hope and the strength of the human spirit through my involvement in the aftermath of large catastrophes, like Ontario's Ice Storm '98, the Oklahoma Bombing, Walkerton Water Crisis, and the September 11th terrorist bombings.

My experiences working with corporate losses - including robbery, violence, fire, accidents, suicide, job loss, mergers, etc. - have taught me about group dynamics and camaraderie.

From the personal traumas such as death, health crises and suicide that change lives forever, I have learned that we do survive and we can re-introduce joy back into our lives.

Long before my formal education and prior to my front-line experiences, I know now that I was being groomed for this career.

Growing up in rural Ontario, I lived happily with my mom, dad, brother and two sisters. For the most part, life was fun, everything seemed simple and clear. I didn't really know what tragedy was, except for the odd crisis that occurred in the barn or field.

My mom and dad brought different gifts of humanity to our home. Both were hard workers and believed that "Life is short; it's what you make of it in the time you have." My mother's motto was "Save a little, spend a little, live lots." I try to hold these beliefs close to my heart.

Dad instilled humour in our household. He would say things like "If you can't laugh, you may as well be dead." Laughter – the best medicine – has helped many of us through difficult times.

Starting in 1995, my nearly idyllic life took a sharp turn. Since then, I have experienced such deep loss in the death of my mother, nephew, father and brother. Prior to these great losses of life, I was immobilized by learning that my then husband was a pedophile, and I suffered the loss of two jobs that I truly loved. All of these loses changed my life.

I'm not sharing these personal losses to instill pity, but to impress upon you that, as difficult as they were and still are, these experiences are a huge piece of who I am.

I have learned to integrate my losses into my life in such a way that I can make the focus more positive than negative. In saying this, even during the difficult moments, which were very dark at times, I was able to find some light, and maintain joy in my life.

That is my purpose in life - to teach others how to maintain joy through their 'life interrupted' experiences.

In putting this book together, I have tried to include as much as I could of what I have learned from family, friends, co-workers, employers, board of directors, strangers, and those people whom I've had the privilege of knowing – even if for a short time – through my work.

Introduction

A friend of mine, a human resources professional, prompted me to write this book to fill a need. While there are many books on process and theory, none of them offers a friendly, simplistic guide for leaders to use as a reference.

A friend of mine, a human resources professional, prompted me to write this book to fill a need. While there are many books on process and theory, none of them offers a friendly, simplistic guide for leaders to use as a reference.

This book offers a holistic approach to understanding how to effectively support people in crisis. It is intended as a guide to a better understanding of some of the sensitive issues that we will be faced with at some time. It is written in the language of those who are experiencing the loss or crisis. They don't talk in clinical terms. They don't use jargon. They speak from the heart.

It is also an attempt to answer some of the questions most frequently posed to me by people in the corporate world, in my support groups, at workshops, face-to-face, or following a keynote presentation.

Most people are uncomfortable with sensitive topics like death, suicide, critical illness, even corporate downsizing and job loss. The reason is simple; they just don't know what to say or do to help. They are afraid of doing the wrong thing and making the situation worse than if they had done nothing at all.

Sometimes there are no plans or policies in place to deal with a crisis at work, or in the personal life of an employee. In fact, in many workplaces policies are developed after a crisis has occurred. If there are policies and benefits in place, make sure they are communicated to all employees, and practiced and updated as a group.

Whether you are in the profession of helping others (as a CEO, manager, nurse, volunteer, human resources professional, emergency responder, etc.) or you do it out of love (as a friend or family member) never lose sight of the fact that you are, first and foremost, human. You have unique thoughts, feelings and emotions, cares and concerns, values and beliefs.

As unique individuals, with our own personal experiences, we look at life through filtered glasses of many colours. Each of us sees every situation and feels every experience differently. While reactions may be similar, no two people ever experience the same event exactly the same way.

Each of us, whether supporting or being supported, needs to sit back and be gentle on ourselves. Each one of us needs to learn more about helping others effectively and appropriately. 'Best practices' are not always the right fit for everyone. We need to be flexible in the way we help each other - from how we communicate to how we follow guidelines.

Even though we may have basic guidelines to follow, we've been taught a certain way, or it's in our company policy, when it comes to working with people, helping them, and helping ourselves maintain or develop and grow healthier and happier lives, nothing in this world is black and white. We need to be mindful of this and always leave room for flexibility in the way we provide support.

We need to take care of ourselves as we take care of others. That means we have to meet the needs of others and make sure our needs are also met.

Most importantly, we need to support our co-workers and employees as well as our friends and family on an everyday basis so they feel valued. Valued and respected people are more productive and work as a team. And it's human nature to want to help and to be part of a team.

Notes

Attitude & Perspective

1

Attitude affects behaviour! There is no way to escape that fundamental truth. Even the attitude: "I should not let my attitude affect my behaviour," affects your behaviour.

"Sometimes people come into your life and you know instantly that they were meant to be there. I want to tell you how much you and your workshop have impacted my life. I couldn't stop thinking of the many valuable pieces of information you shared with us and I knew yesterday when I left your class that my life was changed. I could have listened to you for hours and hours. You have such a presence and an aura that I will never forget. Thank you for everything you taught me yesterday. What an absolute privilege it was to meet you!"

Maria MacLean
Broker Services
Cowan Insurance Brokers Limited

Attitude affects behaviour! There is no way to escape that fundamental truth. Even the attitude: "I should not let my attitude affect my behaviour," affects your behaviour.

Your attitude is one of the most important aspects of working with and helping people. It affects your perspective and the way you react in helping, or not helping, others.

What is attitude?

Attitude is a very personal and internal aspect of your life.

It's about your upbringing, your beliefs and values.

It's how you are feeling on the inside, as a result of things that are going on outside.

It affects the position you take and your reaction in a specific situation.

It includes your mental state, feelings and emotions towards a fact or a situation.

It affects your state of readiness to respond appropriately to a stimulus.

Whether positive or negative, your attitude affects your life and those lives you touch.

Your attitude affects every aspect of your life

A negative attitude can damage the relationship you have with your co-workers, partner, spouse, or anyone you come in contact with. It will definitely impact the intervention you provide and the support you offer to others.

If you want to be helpful to someone, you have to pay attention to your own attitude about the incident.

Attitude is based on perspective.

10

Here are just two of many poignant stories about how attitude affects perspective, and influences the outcome of important decisions.

I was once invited to speak at a bankers' association conference on robbery. Following the presentation, two people approached me to tell me how much they liked the session, and how excited they were for me to meet their CEO.

Awhile later, I met with the CEO. He was definitely the corporate type, white shirt, suit and tie. He was middle-aged, quite plain in fact, and looked like he'd slept in the office overnight. I was surprised at his appearance and thought of the saying - you never get a second chance to make a first impression. With a quick attitude check of my own, I shifted my first impression and gave him the benefit of the doubt.

We shook hands, made small talk and then I had a 20-minute opportunity to outline the robbery program. As usual, I spoke excitedly. As always, my heart was on my sleeve. I spoke of the importance of this type of program and how it can truly make a difference in a person's life, whether they've experienced a robbery or the threat is present. I covered every detail I could to encourage him to seriously consider the program for the many affiliated financial institutions he represented.

When I finished my presentation, the CEO stood up before me, reached out, shook my hand and said in a very nonchalant way, "Thank you for your time, Laurie. What you say is good, however, if I can look down the barrel of a shotgun, so can my staff."

I felt the air being sucked out of my lungs in disbelief. Did he really say what I thought I heard? Here's an example of one person bluntly making the decision for so many, based solely on his own attitude.

◆

Another time, a VP approached me with congratulations on a great presentation. He told me that this type of program would be way down on his to-do list for tellers, since they just replace the tellers if they can't work.

My own attitude adjustment

Both of these situations, and the many other real-life examples, gave me the determination to make a difference and not give up.

I knew that for every person I met, every company I made connection with, I would only be able to provide my services to the converted – to those who consider and respect their employees – their most important asset - as the people who make the business happen.

> Consider and respect employees – the most important asset – people who make business happen.

From that point forward, it became my mission to convert the non-believers with statistics and success stories, and change attitudes!

With my positive attitude shining through, I kept talking to more people, more employers, more CEOs.

13

The win-win attitude of successful organizations

Corporations that see the merit in preparing their people and their workplaces for the inevitable high-stress and crisis situations provide a win-win environment for everyone in the organization. The attitude is - if we support you, we know that, in turn, you will support the organization.

Successful organizations:

+ See themselves as a community, a family, working together towards common goals
+ Establish programs for a healthy workplace environment, focusing on the human element
+ Include not only the technical training needed for the corporation to succeed, but the 'people preparedness' training that is so essential
+ Engage their employees with best leadership practices

- Continually keep the training alive with refreshers and new people-focused programs for the well being of their organization
- Include a sampling of sensitive-subject topics as part of their training options

Nose-up or nose-down – your attitude needs constant evaluation

There's an important instrument used in aircraft to measure the pitch of the plane. It's called an 'altitude meter'. It shows if the aircraft is in a nose-up or a nose-down position.

When flying, especially in adverse conditions, things can feel different to actual fact. You may sense that you are climbing or getting lower, yet sometimes it's hard to tell. The danger is that if you're not in a nose-up position, sooner or later you will crash. The altitude meter measures this aspect and constantly reports to the pilot.

There's a human connection to this, but we'll call it the 'attitude meter.' If your attitude is in a nose-up position, you will rise to new heights, no matter how strong the headwind. If, however, your attitude is in a nose-down position, it will eventually bring you down – even in ideal circumstances. It is this flexibility to constantly evaluate and adjust your attitude to the prevailing situation that leads to success in life.

When you have a negative or one-sided attitude, you may become insensitive and inflexible without realizing it. While you can't control circumstances or other people, you do have 100% control of your attitude.

Notes

Notes

Understanding Grief & Loss

2

The facts of life – To be human is to suffer loss. Or, as George Bernard Shaw put it - one out of one people die. Like it or not, these are raw facts of life. We can either embrace life and all it brings our way, or we can turn away or hide our heads in the sand when something bad happens. My goal is to help people embrace life – the good, the bad and the traumatic.

"Life Interrupted inspired insight and lifted my salon's approach to working with clients who may be experiencing a loss. Laurie's message reduces discomfort when we are faced with grief, both professionally and personally. In helping others, we also help ourselves. Many thanks Laurie for helping us better understand ourselves and others."

Holly Dunn
Owner and Manager
Holly's Hair & Design Systems
Guelph, Ontario

The facts of life – To be human is to suffer loss. Or, as George Bernard Shaw put it - one out of one people die. Like it or not, these are raw facts of life. We can either embrace life and all it brings our way, or we can turn away or hide our heads in the sand when something bad happens. My goal is to help people embrace life – the good, the bad and the traumatic.

Who needs to know?

Over the years, I've been asked to speak about grief and loss to many different groups. Sometimes the group was made up of family and friends who are dealing with the loss of the same person – he was a father to some, a brother to others, a son. Sometimes it's people from different families who have each lost a child, or their mother. There are times when the nature of the loss – such as suicide or murder – brings the people together in the room.

I've had the privilege of speaking to groups of people who work in an industry that deals with death and loss every day, such as funeral home staff, health care professionals, police and other emergency responders.

I have also worked with organizations that need to know how to respond appropriately to take care of the workplace following a trauma or loss. They may have experienced a traumatic incident, or the risk of robbery is high in their line of work and they need to be prepared. They may wish to help a co-worker who has suffered a loss or a serious illness, or help their employees get back to productive work following a critical incident in the workplace.

> There are times when the nature of loss brings people together.

Grieving our losses

Grief is a natural and normal reaction to any type of loss. While grief is the inward thoughts and feelings of loss, mourning is what we do with our grief. It is the 'work' we do with our grief - the outward expression (e.g. crying, talking, rituals, etc.). Most people mistakenly associate grief only with death. In fact, people often grieve changes in their lives - even positive ones – because there is a loss of 'what once was.'

Examples of grief without death

You've just been promoted at work.

You're pleased and proud of yourself. You welcome the additional responsibilities, the new learning and the larger paycheque. On the other hand, you are losing the familiarity of the old job, where you carried out your responsibilities with ease, in the comfort of your co-workers. It's only natural to grieve these losses.

You've just purchased a new home.
It's newer, bigger and ideally located. But it also means leaving the familiar. You could walk around your house in the dark and not stumble. It means moving away from the neighbours who have become part of your daily life. It means, literally, being the new kid on the block for some time. You may very well grieve the loss of these familiarities in your life.

The organization where you work has been sold.
The talk at the water cooler is that there will be downsizing. Job loss, or even the threat of it, makes you feel insecure and you may grieve the comfort and stability you once felt at work.

Your marriage is breaking down.
While your separation or divorce may be amicable, it still involves a lot of changes that you need to get used to. Some of the things you counted on will not be there when you need them. There will be things you have to deal with alone.

The world changed forever on September 11, 2001.

In just a few minutes, the terrorist attacks on the World Trade Centre changed our lives forever. To this day, people are grieving the loss of feeling safe and free in the world they once knew.

Your company is restructuring.

The meeting has been held. Roles and responsibilities will soon be realigned. Job grades and pay may be affected. You are thinking about how much value the company sees in you; how others will see you if your job is rated a lower grade, concerned about loss of respect.

Four basic principles of loss and grief

When I speak to groups or facilitate workshops and training sessions on loss and grief, my sessions explore basic principles. That's because I'm always working with human beings and although the principles are fundamentally similar, each individual and his or her situation is different.

First – To be human is to know loss as part of your life. Along life's path, we encounter many losses, small and large. Some are not as painful as others. Some are devastating and life-altering. What is stressful to us may not be as stressful to others.

Second – We must grieve our losses. If we don't take time to grieve a loss when we experience it, we will likely end up revisiting it at some point in the future, perhaps when we're suffering another loss.

A dear friend of mine is in her 50s. Just after she turned 16, her mother died of cancer. It wasn't sudden, but the family didn't talk about her illness and they weren't prepared for their great loss. My friend, her father and 3 siblings were devastated. Being numb with grief and unable to watch his family in such pain, her father quickly arranged for cremation. There was no visitation, no funeral, and no ceremonial good-bye.

The family didn't speak much about it over the next decade because none of them had properly grieved and still couldn't face the loss. After that, it may have been mentioned now and then, but never explored. If the subject was brought up once in awhile, it was just as quickly changed.

To this day, my friend's heart is heavy with her 35-year-old grief. Over the years, we've talked a lot about her mother. In fact, she's talked more to me than to any member of her family. She knows she needs to do the 'work' of grief for this great life-altering loss and she has been slowly grieving over the years.

Third – The anxiety of a loss can cause so much stress on the body, it can literally change us.

Fourth – To heal, you must acknowledge you are not a patient, that grief is not a disease. You should not expect a prescription or other 'quick fix' to make you better. You must grieve your loss - as long as it takes.

My friend, mentioned above, knows what she needs to do to reconcile her grief journey. She plans to have a ceremonial 'burial' and some type of monument so she can physically say good-bye to her mother and have a place to visit whenever she wants.

A snapshot of the grief journey

Our culture doesn't handle death well, so we are left to find our own resources. When forced to confront the death of a loved one, we need to become an active participant in our own healing.

One basic human desire is that we all want happiness and we want things to stay the same. Another is that we don't want pain and suffering.

> Our culture doesn't handle death well, so we are left to find our own resources.

On those grounds, we have every right to be happy and to use different methods or means to overcome pain and suffering. Although two people may face a similar - or even the same - tragedy, one person may face it more easily than the other, due to his or her attitude and how they view the world.

When we suffer a personal loss, it can't be fixed by material means. That means we must look to our own inner abilities and deepest values to embrace our losses, and thrive in spite of them.

Although I speak from my own experience, I feel that no one has the right to impose his or her beliefs on another person. I will not propose to you that my way is the only way, or that the information I provide is best. The decision is up to you. I will try to explain grief in such a way that you can see how to utilize your own potential to face loss, and how the human mind can confuse us and fight with the heart.

Be an active participant

If you do become an active participant in your own healing, you will experience a renewed sense of meaning and purpose in your life. Life can be renewed, and I have thousands of real-life examples of people who have survived their losses and are leading very happy lives in spite of them.

I invite you to join me as I guide you in an effort to grieve honestly, continue to rebuild your life, and take a few positive 'jewels' away with you.

Notes

Taking Charge
of the Journey

3

This is where the guide begins. Now that you have an understanding of attitudes, perspective, grief and loss, and the part they play in a crisis situation…the following pages provide information that will support you in taking responsibility for evaluating and analyzing, and taking charge of the journey beyond life's interruption.

"As a trainer, Laurie is dynamic and energetic, yet she brings compassion and human sensitivity to difficult issues like grief and suicide. Laurie shares her wealth of knowledge and experience and offers a supportive, compassionate and professional understanding of crisis and loss and how they affect us."

Marion Wright. M.A.
Executive Director
Canadian Mental Health Association

This is where the guide begins. Now that you have an understanding of attitudes, perspective, grief and loss, and the part they play in a crisis situation...the following pages provide information that will support you in taking responsibility for evaluating and analyzing, and taking charge of the journey beyond life's interruption.

The most difficult part of talking about death and loss is that it is a part of your life. The issue of facing it in a peaceful way is a very difficult one.

There seems to be two ways of dealing with loss and suffering:

♦ Simply to try and avoid it - get it out of your mind. This approach only minimizes the loss.

♦ Look at the loss directly, analyze it, make it familiar to you and make it clear that it is a part of your life.

Loss is bound to happen. Instead of avoiding thinking about it, it is better to understand its meaning. We don't often learn this until we've experienced a loss. We may watch the news and see murders and death, but it's removed from us personally. We know it happens all the time, just not to us. This attitude trips us up when it does happen to us. It's what makes the loss of a loved one so very difficult.

Loss is bound to happen. Instead of avoiding thinking about it, it is better to understand its meaning.

This is why we need to learn more about ourselves and our grief journey. It's about being gentle on ourselves and learning how to make a shift in the way we view our loss. With that type of focus, we can reduce the stress and the pain. Rather than avoiding it, we embrace the pain.

Death - the 'ultimate intimacy'

Death itself has been called 'the ultimate intimacy'. Dealing with death evokes feelings unlike any other human experience. The fact is - many people do not know how to respond well to intimacy. Why? We don't want to lose control and our emotions may get the better of us. When someone starts to cry and show emotion, we may become uncomfortable in his or her presence.

After any loss experience, our defense often involves putting on a stoic front and avoiding talk about anything that can create such an intimate setting. Often, the subject is abruptly changed, so you and the person suffering the loss can move on to something else. Even the most talkative person may be dumbstruck in the presence of pain or death.

The grief reaction is physical, emotional, spiritual and psychological. It reaches into our soul. It's important to understand that grief is not a sign of weakness or a lack of faith. Each individual reaction to loss is unique; it depends on our personal life experiences.

Grief is a complex process guided by our experiences, religious beliefs, socio-economic situation, physical health, and the cause of the loss. Anger, love, frustration, fear, loneliness and guilt are all part of grief.

Grieving may cause physical and behavioral changes such as sleep irregularities, loss of or increased appetite, gastro-intestinal disturbances,

> Anger, love, frustration, fear, loneliness and guilt are all part of grief.

'heartache', restlessness, spontaneous crying, irritability, sighing, or muscle tension.

As well as loneliness, hopelessness, helplessness and disappointment, guilt and anger are common emotional responses to grief. You may feel angry with God, your spouse, your children, or with others who are either involved with or totally separate from the loss. You may be angry with yourself. Guilt feelings often accompany or follow anger. You may want to withdraw and be left alone. Not everyone gets angry. Some people may be more focused on disappointment for what they no longer have. Again, it's a personal journey.

Grief isn't something we casually talk about in our lives I'm often asked point blank: "How should I grieve?" There is no defined way to grieve, nor is there a defined timeframe. Again, grieving is as individual as you are.

> After coming to a grief support group of mine for four weeks, a woman told me that her friends and family were concerned that she seemed to be getting worse. She was talking about her loss more and crying a lot. Simply put, she was doing the 'work' of grief by mourning her loss.

Our death-denying society

In our death-denying society, we tend to speak in euphemisms - words that are more comfortable or safe - so as not to offend or hurt. The reality of the word "death," as harsh as it may seem, is the word that is most helpful in accepting it.

It's better to say "he died," rather than "he's passed on" or "left us." If you're not sure what to say, listen and speak the language of the person who has suffered the loss. (For more information, please refer to the chapter entitled *Communicating Effectively During and Following a Crisis.*)

When the loss involves a death, each of us grieves in our own time. For those on the outside looking in, it may seem like the grieving process has gone on too long, or not long enough. We must always remember that everyone grieves in their own way, in their own time frame. No two people grieve the same. No loss affects two lives in the same way.

Following a crisis or loss, others may want the person to be the way they used to be more quickly or completely than they are able.

A lady I knew was grieving her daughter's death. She was on bereavement leave from her job for a couple of weeks. After returning to work, her supervisor was upset that she was so different and actually said, "I want the old you back". The truth is that this person's world is different now that her daughter has died. The fact is she will never be exactly the same as she was before her loss.

When someone we know dies, things will never be the same. How could they be the same? This doesn't mean that life is going to be dark and dismal forever. It means that an adjustment is necessary and with that adjustment, life is different.

It's often our own fears that keep us from supporting others. In this case, the supervisor may not have known how to offer support, so she opted for getting things back to where they were, where she was more comfortable, where there was no loss.

How to support others

For the most part, it's human nature to want to be helpful to others. Whether it's a kind gesture, a caring word, or just giving someone your time, it feels good knowing that you've helped in some way. But caring and supporting someone experiencing a loss of any type is not often an easy task. Sometimes we hesitate, or don't offer support at all – because we just don't know what to say or what to do.

> Sometimes we hesitate or don't offer support, because we just don't know what to say or do.

I have learned a lot from my own grief experiences, from working with others through their losses, and from teachings on the subject. Here are a few of the many helpful ways to support someone who is experiencing the loss of a loved one, friend or co-worker.

Listen with your heart.

It's important to know that you don't have to be a therapist to care and to listen. Whether you have your professional or personal hat on, in that awkward moment when someone tells you that they have lost a friend, acquaintance or loved one and you don't know what to say or do, the best way to support them is to listen. Be there in body, mind and spirit.

This doesn't mean that you can't make a sound. It's essential that the person you support knows that you are connecting with them. It is also important to keep your body still while you are listening. In emotional situations like this, some people have twitches, need to tap their foot, swivel on a chair or look around the room. Just try to be still. It's a test of your own skills and self-control.

I recently watched an interview with Clint Eastwood in which he stated that standing still was one of the most difficult exercises he had to practice. He was on a stage with a line of people and the director told them not to move, just stand and be still. He shared how it was extremely difficult at first, how your mind races and you have to talk yourself into being still. Once he was able to control his mind and relax his body, he found the exercise to be very helpful and found a new place for his own discipline.

This means listening from a place where the person you are supporting can share their story in the way they need to speak about their loss. Even if you have experienced a loss yourself, resist the urge to tell your story. You may want to share just a snippet – that you've had a loss or experienced a death – as it might help the person feel less isolated. Keep in mind, however, that timing is everything.

Just be still and let them talk. Your willingness to listen is the most precious gift you can offer. When someone is telling their story, make sure there are no distractions.

Listen and you may notice that the story is sometimes both heavy and light, or it could be very heavy. Pay attention to how the person looks after sharing the story. Sometimes they may seem tired. More often, they look like a great weight has been lifted.

It's not about you in that moment. It's about giving of yourself to help someone else. As the old adage goes: the reason we have two ears and only one mouth is so we can listen more and talk less.

Share stories about the person who died.

Encouraging people to share their grief over and over is like peeling away the layers of pain and the intensity of the loss. It's not unusual for the grieving person to feel a little more relief each time the story is shared. It helps them to connect their head and heart.

After my brother's funeral, many guests came out
to his home. There was one gentleman in
particular, who sat with a group of us around the
table, and shared so many stories about my
brother that I learned about him in a new light. It
was so uplifting to hear about my brother, as others
knew him.

A written note is a comforting way to express that you care.

It's different from a phone call, as a note can
be read and re-read and bring comfort when
it's needed. Share a story about the person in
a note. Even writing the deceased person's
name often provides comfort to the person
receiving your message.

When someone in the workplace dies, it's a
wonderful gesture to have employees write in
a book and share a note or story about the
person, then present the book to the family as
a keepsake. It gives the family a more intimate
view of how their loved one spent his
working hours, how others viewed him, and
the fact that he made an impression on others

around him. For employees, it gives them an outlet to express their feelings and thoughts.

Honour the deceased with a memorial service.

A memorial service is a meaningful way of involving the workplace in offering support to the employees as well as the family and friends of the person who died. That's also what a funeral does; it brings people together and provides an aid in the emotional healing. If you can't attend the funeral or memorial service, you can support them in other ways.

When planning a memorial, talk to the family about what you'd like to do to honour the person who died. Remember, people going through a crisis still can think! Having the family's approval removes any doubt and makes everyone more comfortable while honouring the deceased person.

I remember a story where a woman was killed during a robbery in a financial institution. The building was taped up, the office was moved to a new location, and no memorial service was provided. This was a sad way to show respect for the person who died and to all those who had a relationship with her. It was like placing a large band-aid on life, to cover the hurt.

Phone and visit often.

You've heard the saying – at times like this, you soon learn who your real friends are. Following the funeral, the grieving person may experience further loss, as friends, relatives, co-workers and family get back to their normal routines. You can't because yours is a 'new normal'. The feelings of emptiness and loneliness can be overwhelming. Your call or visit will be a wonderful gift, perhaps an antidote, to help ease those deep feelings of loneliness.

Encourage dialogue.

Don't just make small talk. Offering genuine support means allowing the bereaved person to talk about their loss if they want to. (For more information, please refer to the chapter entitled *Communicating Effectively During and Following a Crisis.*)

Think before you speak.

While we've already said to encourage dialogue, sometimes saying nothing is better than saying the wrong thing. Sometimes what we say can minimize the sense of loss and further frustrate a person. The brain says they know it's not intentional, but the heart says: "Ouch, that really hurt."

Misunderstandings from words alone can be hurtful to someone experiencing loss. I have listed some common phrases that I continue to hear again and again. This tells me that people are really trying to care, but they just don't know what to say to help or support.

Even the bereaved may come up with their own phrases so as not to burden those around them.

What NOT to say:

- Things happen for a reason.
- Don't feel bad.
- You're young. You can always remarry.
- You still have another child.
- Life goes on, so must you.
- He's in a better place.
- She led a full life.
- Be grateful you had your job this long.
- You have to get on with it.
- Oh well, what can you do?
- Been there, done that.
- It was God's will.
- She's not suffering anymore.
- I know what you mean.
- I don't understand you anymore.

Be flexible.

When wearing the corporate hat, sometimes decisions are made with only the workplace in mind. If an employee is having difficulty performing responsibilities, frequently calls in sick, or is at risk of endangering himself or others in the workplace, a decision may have to be made to remedy the situation.

But, if management hasn't bought into the "understanding" side of managing, a quick decision to lay-off or dismiss the employee may be made as a quick fix. Perhaps what the employee really needs is an opportunity to have someone help them for a short period of time, to move to flex time for awhile, or assume less responsibilities for now or just to listen to them.

It's important for management to talk to the employee about their thoughts and feelings and what they may be having the most difficulty with.

It's okay to show that you care about employees.

It could be low concentration, feeling inadequate, feeling sad or depressed. The key is to let them know that they are being supported.

As mentioned previously, we cannot set a time frame for when someone will feel better or be back on track. For some people, getting back to work and being focused is helpful to them; for others it's an impossibility at this time.

Sometimes the grieving person wants to do something radical, like sell the house, move away, change jobs, or make large purchases. Unless these changes are absolutely necessary, it may be wise to leave any major decisions and changes for the first year. As mentioned earlier in this chapter, major changes can bring added stress.

Keeping in mind that everyone is unique and no two people will grieve the same way, here's a story about a widower who did make an immediate and radical change in his life – and it worked for him!

This gentleman was his wife's caregiver. When he wasn't at work, he was at home taking care of her. After her death, he felt that the house was bringing him too much sadness, and he just needed to start fresh. He sold his home and moved into a condominium. He told me it was the best thing he could have done. He still has her photos and their wonderful memories, but his new home has given him peace. It was what he felt would be best for him and, more often than not, we do know what is truly best for us.

Be careful what you read.

For those who have experienced the death of a loved one, the search for answers is at the forefront everyday. Why me? How will I ever get past this? What can I do to stop these feelings? When will I feel better? Will I ever get back to the way I was?

While there are many good resources available, sometimes we can become inundated with self-help books. My suggestion is to read a book (even this one) and only take from it what feels comfortable for you. I can't stress enough that everyone is unique and every loss is experienced differently. Just because something worked for someone else, it may not be right for you.

Depending on what you read, you'll get very differing opinions. For example, some authors present the psychological aspect of learning about grief and trauma into phases or stages. When describing the 'reconciliation' stage, one book lists 12 criteria while another lists only eight. Each author writes from his/her own research, background, understanding and experiences. Some authors even include time frames for each phase. These books are meant as teaching guides, but as a reader in pain you might look at this information as fact and misunderstand that this may not be a fit for you.

For individuals who are trying to find answers about why they feel and act they way they do, this may not be the most helpful information to read. I often hear people say, "Oh, she's in the shock phase" or "he's in the impact stage". Be gentle with your interpretation of any book.

You are a unique individual;
you do not have
to make yourself fit into
anyone else's phases or
stages. Try to understand that
each day is going to be
different, and then there may
be days or weeks that seem
to feel the same. The time
frame will be your own.

> Each of us is a
> unique
> individual; we
> do not have to
> make
> ourselves fit
> into anyone
> else's phases
> or stages.

There is so much reading material out there,
it's over-whelming. And, since people
generally believe what is printed, it can
actually make your grief journey more
difficult. You may become exhausted, trying
to be the way the book says you should be.
Or, the information may be written for
therapists, from a clinical perspective, or for
educational purposes only.

Additional tips on supporting others

Don't judge people. Sometimes our own beliefs can get in the road to helping.

Have an ethical intention to assist.

Don't interpret, analyze or diagnose what the person is saying.

Empathize in terms of validating feelings. Tell them it's okay to feel the way they do.

Remember to control the environment to keep the person safe. There's no need for onlookers.

Make sure you comprehend what the person is saying and when in doubt, ask.

Never probe, question or interrogate.

Be interestED, not interestING.

Use all of the listening skills to make an effort to understand.

Make sure that the people you assist do benefit from your help.

In our suffering and in helping others through theirs, we can never lose sight of the fact that we are first and foremost 'human.' We have hearts and minds. The journey is not about torturing ourselves. We may run into the intellectual side fighting the heartfelt side. We shouldn't let that happen. Just listen and feel with all your heart.

Notes

Communicating Effectively During & Following a Crisis

4

The desire to help others is part of human nature, but many people avoid it because they don't know what to say or do to offer effective support. Knowing how to communicate effectively is important in any situation; it is essential when you're helping others through a crisis.

"As a facilitator, Laurie has an uncanny ability to draw you in as a dear friend. Her passion for helping others makes you comfortable in baring your soul to her, as she does with her personal stories and human anecdotes. She takes dark topics and injects them with light. There's no doubt in my mind that Laurie is in the right profession."

Deirdre Lindsay, B.A.
Communications Consultant

The desire to help others is part of human nature, but many people avoid it because they don't know what to say or do to offer effective support. Sometimes it is our own fears that keep us away. Knowing how to communicate effectively is important in any situation; it is essential when you're helping others through a crisis.

It doesn't take much to tune-up your communication skills so you can respond confidently and appropriately to help others - and make a difference.

Here are a few things you need to know about communicating effectively during and following a crisis.

The 'chemical cocktail' of stress

Following a crisis, people are often confused by all the conflicting emotional responses around them. They are, in fact, responding normally to an abnormal situation. The 'fight-or-flight' response is a typical reaction to crisis. It's a biological preparation for fighting the danger, or running from it.

While individuals will react differently to every situation, based on their personalities and life experiences, here's what's happening to your body chemistry in a stressful situation:

The anatomy of stress

Three systems jump into action during a stressful experience, the:
* Nervous system
* Endocrine system
* Hypothalamus releases endorphins.

The physical response to stress[1]

With all this going on inside, it's not difficult to understand why the physical response to a stressful situation is called a 'chemical cocktail:'
* Adrenaline (epinephrine), cortisol, and other hormones pour into the bloodstream, mixing a "Chemical Cocktail" of alarm that reinforces and prolongs the stress reaction.

---

[1] Adapted from the Tactical Edge, by Charles Remsberg

* Certain blood vessels tighten and others expand as the circulatory system diverts blood away from the skin surface, extremities and digestive organs.
* The blood is channeled to the large muscle groups – those most closely related to strength and speed.
* The heart and lungs work harder and faster to rush fresh nutrients to these tissues and clear away waste.
* The spleen discharges more red blood cells into the bloodstream to increase the oxygen supply.
* The liver releases stored sugar to boost energy.
* Blood pressure skyrockets.
* Muscles tense, especially in the lower back, neck and shoulders, staying near the threshold of action in anticipation of movement.
* The sweat glands kick in as the body tries to cool itself.

'Sympathy' versus 'Empathy'

To support others effectively through a crisis, it's also important to know the difference between 'sympathy' and 'empathy'.

Sympathy is when one person assumes or shares the feelings of another person.

Empathy is the ability to understand a person's feelings, as if they were your own.

As someone who offers support, you want to be empathetic and even use the language of the person you are supporting.

> When my brother spoke of his son who had died in an automobile accident, he always said "when Thomas was killed" not "when Thomas died". He corrected me every time until I realized that he was speaking the way he had to in order to deal with his loss. If I was to offer support, I needed to speak his language.

More than words can say

When we communicate, there's a lot more involved than just words. In fact, some studies conclude that words make up only a small fraction of our communications. The three main components of communication and their respective 'weighting' is said to be:

7%	WORDS
38%	TONE
55%	NON-VERBAL

Non-verbal communication includes eye contact, listening, body language, facial expressions, and so on.

Four simple steps for communicating effectively

#1 - Listen & Learn

Since words are only a small fraction of the communication process (7%), that puts a lot of responsibility on non-verbal exchanges such as listening. How can you become a better listener? Here are 10 simple ways to enhance the listening process:

+ Take time and make time.
+ Eliminate distractions.
+ Make eye contact, but don't stare.
+ Nod or use minimal encouragers ("uh huh," "oh," "I see").
+ Question when appropriate, but don't interrupt.
+ Be patient.
+ Respond without judgment or bias.
+ Listen with your whole body for cues like tone, emphasis on certain words, loudness, body language, etc.
+ Reflect and check for feelings.
+ Empower the person by allowing them to find their own way.

Other helpful hints about listening
Minimal encouragers, like "uh huh", "oh", "I see", let the other person know that you are listening and you're interested in what they have to say. They keep the conversation going, encourage the other person to talk, maintain flow

without interruption, and show that you are paying attention.

Use "I" messages as a perception check. For example: "I'm having difficulty understanding" is better than "You're confusing me."

Rephrase for clarity, by restating what the person has said using different words. Why rephrase? Relaying back what you heard shows that you are truly listening and that you want to understand. It shows respect. Respect builds trust and that enhances the relationship. It also allows the other person to hear what he or she is saying, perhaps for the first time.

#2 – 'Hear' the silence

You don't have to fill every silence. In fact, you shouldn't interrupt it. Let the silence go on for a few moments and allow the other person to initiate conversation. It's always better to say nothing at all than to blurt out something inappropriate for the sake of breaking the silence.

Silence is a powerful communication technique

It lets others know that you're there and you're listening.

It gives them permission to take their time, think things through, come up with options and solutions, and go at their own pace.

It gives you time to observe, think and plan.

Interrupting silence can lead to a communication breakdown

If you're not 'listening' to the silence, you might be missing something and that can lead to a communication breakdown. Keep in mind that interrupting the silence can be interpreted as many things, including:

- ❖ You're not listening fully to me.
- ❖ You're ignoring the crucial relationship between my thoughts, feelings and actions.
- ❖ You're interrupting me before I'm finished thinking or talking.

* You're just filling the silence.
* You're interrupting my train of thought.
* You're finishing my sentences and assuming you're following my train of thought.

When supporting others, you don't have to have an answer or reply for everything. Sometimes you're most helpful by just 'being there'. Listen carefully to the silence; it speaks volumes!

#3 - Ask the right questions

Questions should be used to encourage communication, to clarify a point, fill a gap, or move things along. Your questions should never be too personal, or used to control the communication by deciding what will and will not be discussed.

Five tips on asking the right questions

Ask for clarification when you don't understand.

Ask open-ended questions that can't easily be answered with "yes" or "no." For example: "So, if I understand you correctly…"

> Ask, ask, ask…

Don't push for answers. If the other person doesn't want to answer a question, move on.

Ask questions that place the responsibility to talk on the other person. For example: "Can you tell me more about …?"

Ask questions that guide the person towards constructing new alternatives and finding their own solutions. For example, "What are some things you've thought of?" is more empowering than "What if you did this…?"

Questions that encourage communication

Sometimes, just wording the questions right makes all the difference. The following questions encourage communication:

* How can I help you?
* What is the situation as you see it?
* What would you like me to do for you?
* Where would you be most comfortable talking?
* I have no idea what this must be like for you; I've never been in this situation. Can you tell me what it's like?
* You must have been very close to her. What was she like?

#4 - Realize your power to empower

When someone has a problem or is going through a difficult time, he or she must also 'own' the solution. Help others explore their options and examine their feelings, rather than giving them solutions. Keep in mind that just because something worked for you in the past, it doesn't mean it is appropriate for a different person in a different situation.

True helpers are not rescuers; they empower others to recognize that they are able to regain control of their own lives.

Notes

Notes

The Importance of Suicide Intervention Awareness Training

5

Remember the old wives' tale: a suicidal person never talks about his or her intentions? Well, that's exactly what it is — a story, a tale, pure fiction. Suicidal people send out signals...

"Laurie's genuine care and concern for people rings true in both her message and her delivery. She is dealing with important but difficult topics, yet it takes only moments for Laurie to break the ice and bring the room on board. Her personal stories help to humanize the topic and bring the training to life."

David Beal
Risk Management
Ontario School Boards' Insurance Exchange

Remember the old wives' tale: a suicidal person never talks about his or her intentions? Well, that's exactly what it is – a story, a tale, pure fiction. Suicidal people send out signals, there are behavioural changes, there may be physical changes, and there are always signs and symptoms that all is not well. So, what are these if not an invitation to help?

Almost everyone knows of someone who has died by suicide. And there are many more who have attempted.

Did you know?

- In any given year, approximately 6% of the entire population has serious thoughts of suicide.
- One in nine has seriously considered suicide.
- Four to 5% of all people attempt suicide in their lifetime.
- More people die by suicide than in the entire armed conflict worldwide.
- Approximately the same numbers of people die from suicide as from traffic accidents.

- For every person who dies by suicide, there are as many as 100 times more who injure themselves from non-fatal suicidal behaviour.
- Suicide affects people of all ages, of all races, and both sexes.
- Not everyone has a mental illness who takes his or her own life.

For additional information on suicide intervention, please refer to www.livingworks.net LivingWorksEducation Inc., Calgary Alberta.

Coming to terms with suicide

Loss is always difficult. But when someone you love dies by suicide, it's especially hard to accept. The legacy of a suicide often includes a lifetime of sadness, anger, confusion and grief.

Family, friends and co-workers may be thrown into a spin of disbelief as they adjust to the sudden loss. Along with that, they may have to reconcile their own feelings of helplessness. They couldn't do anything to help because they didn't know the person was suicidal. Or, they may have noticed something was wrong, but they just didn't know what to say or do to help. Often, in retrospect, they recognize the red flags.

How suicide affects the workplace

When you consider the statistics, the potential for suicide affecting any workplace is high. In 'bottom-line' terms, the emotional costs can add up, with long- and short-term absences, illness, low productivity, morale issues and recruiting and rehiring costs when people leave the job.

Following a suicide, it's especially difficult for employees to feel that it's okay to talk about it. Depending how it's handled, they may just keep their thoughts and feelings to themselves. It's important to allow the opportunity for staff to talk to each other about the death and their thoughts and feelings about it, without keeping it a secret as if it didn't happen.

A pro-active workplace incorporates 'people preparedness' into their policies and training programs.

Someone shared with me that two people he once worked with killed themselves. One was gay and the other person was diagnosed with Aids. No one talked about the suicides, and no assistance or support was provided to the staff. It left everyone with unreconciled feelings of shock and loss and it was difficult to grieve the losses. The feelings are still in this person's life.

Recognizing opportunities to help

Suicide intervention awareness training isn't rocket science. We can all learn how to do it! It is a misconception that only professionals such as police, fire, ambulance, counselors, doctors and nurses can stop someone from attempting suicide or intervene. Everyday, you and I are around co-workers, friends, family and other loved-ones who may need our help. We simply need to learn to recognize the signs and understand how to help. It's not about therapy, it's about helping.

When someone exhibits signs of suicidal behaviour, it doesn't mean you have to immediately phone 911, or contact your Human Resources personnel. Sometimes it just takes a caring gesture, or not being afraid to ask the appropriate questions to help. Or, it may be knowing the right steps to take to get the person the referral he or she needs. Effective suicide awareness training can help your workplace develop the skills, knowledge, tools and confidence needed to recognize opportunities to help, so employees don't hesitate to reach out and offer support when it's needed.

> A story that stands out in my mind involves a young woman who was going through a difficult time at work and at home. Her home life was stressed financially and her husband was going to claim bankruptcy. She confided in a co-worker whom she knew she could trust.

> After about a month of sharing her story with her co-worker and confiding in him, she told him that she didn't want to live anymore and that it would be easier for her just to die. Instead of saying anything, he just listened and hoped that she would get over this day and things would be better tomorrow.

The day after she shared her story, they both attended a general meeting at work with about 50 others. Just before the break, the co-worker told me that the suicidal woman leaned over and whispered that tonight was the night she was going to kill herself. The co-worker didn't know what to do, if anything at all. He wondered if she was crying "wolf" for attention. After all, she had been quite depressed.

The co-worker discreetly left the room and reported the story to the human resources department. Soon after, there was utter chaos. The emergency responders came running into the room and took the woman away.

Why was this situation handled this way?

The company policies stated that anyone who is suicidal on the premises was to be reported immediately and that emergency response would be contacted to take care of the situation.

The problem with this situation was that no one had spoken with the woman to understand exactly where she was at risk.

When the co-worker was telling me this story, he was so full of regret that he hadn't responded differently. Since then, he has attended the suicide intervention training and feels much better prepared to help.

Even though this isn't a happy-ending story, it does demonstrate the fact that suicide is real. The topic of suicide has been ignored or avoided far too long because it's not comfortable for us to talk about someone wanting to take his or her life. We can't understand how anyone could have thoughts of suicide.

> The topic of suicide has been avoided for far too long.

It is comforting to know that countries around the world are learning more and more about suicide and how to help people who are having thoughts about killing or harming themselves.

With the best training, the competency skills that we learn will make us less afraid of helping someone and understanding how serious suicide really is.

'Red flags' that suicidal people wave

Suicide seldom occurs without warning. That's why everyone should be aware of the 'red flags' and know what to say and do to help. That doesn't mean you need to know how to counsel. Rather, it's about being a gatekeeper, recognizing the signs, and knowing how to offer effective support to keep someone safe. It also means knowing how to refer the suicidal person for the appropriate help he or she needs through this difficult time. Here are some physical, emotional and behavioural 'red flags' to be aware of.

Physical signs may include:

* Neglect of personal appearance
* A sudden change in the manner of dress, especially when the new style is completely out of character
* Chronic or unexplained illness, aches and pains
* A sudden, inexplicable weight gain or loss
* A sudden change in appetite – not eating, binge-eating

Emotional signs may include:

- A sense of hopelessness, helplessness, or futility
- An inability to enjoy or appreciate friendships
- Drastic mood swings, sudden outbursts
- Anxiousness, extreme tension, agitation
- Lethargy or unusual tiredness
- Personality changes (e.g. from outgoing to withdrawn, from polite to rude, from compliant to rebellious, from well-behaved to "acting-out")
- Loss of the ability to concentrate, daydreaming
- Depression, sadness
- Loss of rational thought
- Feelings of guilt or failure
- Self-destructive thoughts
- Exaggerated fears of disease or physical impairment
- Feelings of worthlessness or of being a burden
- Loss of enjoyment from activities formerly enjoyed

Behavioral signs may include:

- Threatening suicide, suicide attempts
- Hoarding pills, hiding weapons, describing how they are going to kill themselves
- Making a will, writing poetry or stories about suicide or death
- Quietly putting affairs in order, or 'taking care of business'
- Decreased activity, isolation
- Loss of interest in hobbies, sports, work, achievement, etc.
- Unexplained use of drugs or alcohol
- Withdrawal from family and friends, purposely driving others away
- Change in eating and/or sleeping habits
- Change in friendships
- Running away from home, skipping school, missing work
- More accident-prone, increased risk-taking
- Careless driving, car accidents
- Dangerous use of firearms (e.g. playing 'Russian roulette')
- Sexual promiscuity
- Giving away prized possessions
- Sudden personality change
- Preoccupation with thoughts of death

Offering support in a time of need

Those who are informed pick up on the signals sent by a suicidal person. Armed with awareness training, they are confident in supporting a co-worker, friend or family member in a time of need, and they know how to get them the help they need.

Aside from removing any feelings of helplessness, it is personally rewarding to know that you have done everything you can to help – and that you may have saved a life!

Notes

A Team Approach to Helping People in Crisis

5

Most organizations have some type of contingency plan in place for disaster recovery. This usually involves tactical and strategic planning. However, they also need to consider the importance of the 'people' component ...

22

"Laurie genuinely brings the human touch and feeling element into her presentations. When educating others about trauma and crisis situations, Laurie's delivery style is very appropriate and reassuring for her clients."

Don Maisonville
Principal, Level Five Strategic Partners Inc.

Most organizations have some type of contingency plan in place for disaster recovery. This usually involves tactical and strategic planning such as computer backup, a safe for money and valuables, off-site storage of important documents, video surveillance, and so on. However, they also need to consider the importance of the 'people' component of disaster recovery planning and understand the value it brings to the organization.

There are many different types of teams and they are called by many names. Whether yours is part of Disaster Recovery, Business Continuity, Crisis, or Emergency Response, Community Response Team, it's important to note that The Human Element for People Preparedness should be part of the name. As with any leadership team, there is going to be emotion when a crisis hits. Understanding the 'human element' is the necessary component for assisting the people and supporting the team.

How Your Workplace Benefits

Productivity, morale, and relationships at work and at home suffer following any critical incident. Managers, team leaders, supervisors, and others need to know how to appropriately support staff through a crisis in the workplace, help them survive the trauma and get everyone back to productive work more quickly.

Open and honest communication before, during and after a crisis helps build camaraderie – and that means happy, healthy, motivated workers who care about each other and the workplace.

Effective crisis response can minimize corporate expenses related to short- and long-term absences, reduced productivity, increased medical claims, hiring and training costs if employees resign, litigation, etc.

The role of the crisis response team

An organization's crisis team plays an important role in the immediate aftermath of a crisis affecting the workplace. When a crisis hits the workplace, it takes time for emergency responders (police, fire, and ambulance) to get to the scene. While you're waiting, time doesn't stand still. In fact, what your organization's response team does, and how they communicate on the frontline, is critical to the impact the crisis has on your workplace. During a crisis, your well-defined and well-rehearsed team will be the 'calm during the storm'.

It's also important that the team acquires the skills necessary to support others before an emergency occurs. That involves recognizing the different responses people have in a crisis situation and understanding how to support them. It means listening and communicating effectively, not taking their control away, and knowing how to empower others. It's understanding how to make people feel safe, and knowing how to get additional help for yourself and others when necessary.

By reducing stress in a crisis situation, the response team helps maintain control.

Five important components of a successful crisis response program are:
* Designing a well-defined plan
* Putting clear policies in place
* Communicating the plan to all staff
* Selecting the team
* Practicing and auto-pilot training
* Self-care programs in place

Designing a well-defined plan

When a crisis affects the workplace, a well-defined plan will provide the tools your organization needs to help your staff focus, make clear decisions that positively affect the outcome of the situation, support others during and following the incident - and survive!

Putting clear policies in place

Whether management sets the policies, or they are designed by human resources, staff members from all levels of the organization, or an outside firm, they need to be clearly understood, written in plain language, and communicated throughout the organization. They also need to be updated regularly, as the organization grows and changes, and as employees leave and new ones are hired.

Communicating the plan

Another major component of a pro-active disaster recovery program involves communicating the plan and any changes, updates, or additions to all staff at regular intervals. The plan should be communicated to everyone involved in the organization, including part-time and full-time staff, contracted employees, new recruits, student help, occasional staff, etc. Organizations may use staff meetings, training sessions, emails, newsletters, training materials or other communication methods to get the plans out to all staff. Questions should be invited, and answers to those questions provided to all staff. As well, someone should

> Communicate to everyone involved in the organization.

be responsible for reviewing and updating the information on a regular basis.

Selecting the team

For smaller organizations, the team might involve everyone. In larger companies, team members might be selected from each department or area. It's important to spend some time considering who should be on the team, and how many people should be involved. There should be representatives from all levels of the organization, including management, front-line workers, human resources professionals and anyone else who will bring value to the team. It's also important to have a contingency in place to cover absent team members, replacements for those who are no longer with the organization, alternates to cover for someone who needs a break, etc.

When selecting members for your team, keep in mind that not everyone is suitable for this role. Your team should be well rounded, with members representing all levels of the organization as well as people with different strengths.

In a high school, for example, the team should include administrative staff and maintenance workers. Often these groups know the students personally, sometimes more than a teacher or the principal.

In manufacturing, it's not always the manager or supervisor who knows the employees best. It's more likely to be those who work side-by-side, in the same department, or on the same shift. In this example, team representation should be included from each shift.

Practicing and auto-pilot training

All staff should practice the procedures as well as any specific risk management techniques geared to the organization.

A corporation, for example, should know the procedures to follow in the event of a crisis situation. They should know what to do and what not to. They should know when to call for emergency assistance, how to make the call, and how to secure the area.

Continually update the plan.

To continually update and improve the plan, there should be a process for feedback and a 'post-mortem' following any crisis.

Regular rehearsals help familiarize everyone with the procedures. Then, when an incident occurs and you find it difficult to focus, your autopilot training will kick in. Practicing and training also help people focus on the situation, their safety and the safety of others. It's important to recognize the signs of impending trouble, so you can minimize your risk.

Qualities to look for when selecting your team members include:
  * Trustworthy, understands the importance of confidentiality
  * Flexible
  * Focused
  * High tolerance for stress

- Training/background in stress management, crisis intervention, group dynamics,
- Communication, emotional responses to crisis, physical responses to trauma,
- Characteristics of a critical incident, stress management, crisis communication, etc.
- Works well in a team situation and independently
- Highly supportive of the team and other team members
- Able to think rationally 'on the fly'
- Psychologically stable
- Supported by management
- Good and quick decision-maker
- Able to handle raw emotion
- Able to handle blood, guts and gore
- Pays attention to detail
- High energy
- Honesty/integrity
- Controlled demeanor
- Resilient
- Decisive
- Innovative

Responsibilities of the Team

Have your plan in place. Make sure it is accessible and easy to follow – especially in a crisis situation. When people are functioning in high-stress situations, searching through a binder with tabs and small font is very difficult. Clear instructions and simple statements, in a large font, is much easier to follow.

Contact the appropriate emergency responders (e.g. fire, police, ambulance, tow truck, etc.).

Contact families, other plants/offices/ branches, community groups, etc.

Ensure a trained PR spokesperson from the organization is prepared to inform the media of the situation and keep them apprised throughout. The team should ensure that any media questions are directed to the PR spokesperson and that everyone follows this procedure.

Effectively communicate policies and procedures to all staff, from part-timers to the CEO, student help and contractors, and all new employees. Make sure any changes or updates are also communicated.

Build in a 'contingency plan' for your team, to accommodate vacations, illness, staff changes, corporate growth, etc.

Help select the appropriate team members to ensure a full compliment.

Keep the program 'alive' by ensuring that the plan is reviewed, updated, and communicated on a regular basis.

Conduct a 'post-mortem' following each critical incident.

Provide a report so that all staff members know what happened, recommendations for change, what was done well, suggestions, etc. Research and pre-select any outside professionals, in case follow-up or referral is necessary.

Establish a 'command post' that is safe, accessible, and close to but not in the building that houses the organization. (It's best to select 3 locations ahead of time, in case one becomes inaccessible, etc.) This is where the team meets, coordinates recovery efforts, 'checks in' at specified intervals to assess and re-group, conducts 'practice drills', etc.

Screen and pre-select the certified frontline professionals/interventionists you may need to support and/or train your staff.

When external support is needed

External crisis responders should be selected pro-actively, that is before a critical incident occurs, before you actually need them.

Here are some questions your team should ask of any external crisis responders who are being considered:
* Do you have experience with the situation at hand?
* Do you have a frontline designation or certification such as Certified Trauma

Specialist (CTS) or are you trained in Critical Incident Stress Reactions (CISR)?
* Do you have 3 references I can call? (Always call more than one reference to make sure they check out.)
* Do you believe in referring people to other agencies, once your job is completed?
* Can you explain concepts of frontline intervention?
* Do you have lots of experience on the frontlines?
* Do you understand your role in our intervention model?

When interviewing an Employee Assistance Program (EAP) organization, it is important to make certain they will be open to working with other specialized experts or organizations. Particularly in dramatic crisis, specialized expertise might be a better fit for the situation. For example, during a major ice storm when everything shut down and people were dramatically displaced from their daily lives – life was interrupted. Specialized expertise to deal with a different kind of grief and loss was required.

This type of support is also important to smaller companies. If you do not have an EAP, consider the resources within your community; ask other employers who they use, form a relationship with a trusted supplier of these specialized services before you are faced with a crisis.

Frontline professionals should have trained field staff who have had experience 'in the trenches.' They should be professionally trained, used to chaos and 'raw' emotional responses. It takes a special type of person who can think on their feet, have a clear understanding of 'empathy' versus 'sympathy', and be able to perform under extreme pressure.

In conclusion

Having a plan in place, that includes a trained and confident response team, is directly related to the short- and long-term impact the crisis has on the workplace and, ultimately, the organization's bottom line.

Notes

Notes

Index

Editor's note

In this intimate account, Laurie uses her personal loss experiences - from the death of her mom, dad, brother and nephew, to the breakdown of her marriage, and job loss - to help others through theirs. She has spoken about "surviving loss" to thousands of people. She has walked alongside and gently supported many in their grief journeys and also learned from them.

As her editor, I have learned a lot about loss and grief that cannot be gleaned from books and research. As her friend, I have learned that we must grieve every loss - even if decades later. I have learned that when someone we love dies, our lives are forever changed, and the pain goes from intense to that of lesser intensity. I have come to realize not to define myself by my losses, but to learn about myself through the journey.

"Finally, someone has broken the awkward silence! Laurie has put a lot of hard work, energy and passion into creating this guide that is so desperately needed in every workplace and home. After all, suffering loss is part of our mortal reality. For most of us, it's a genuine struggle - we truly want to help others in their times of need, but we're so afraid of saying or doing the wrong thing. So we don't. Now, we have a simple guide, written for the layperson, with so much to say about the intricacies and commonalties of human nature and the strength of the human spirit. It's like taking CPR for the soul – now I know I can help others and make a difference."

Deirdre Lindsay
Freelance Writer

Acknowledgements

First and foremost, I am indebted to the
thousands of people who have confided in me
and trusted me with their personal grief and
loss experiences. Walking alongside these
special people, who have shared their journeys
and their most intimate stories, has taught me
a new language of grief and loss. They have
shown me how to hold onto life and how I
can help others do the same.

I continue to learn from those who have
participated in my workshops, coaching
sessions, grief support groups and keynotes. I
have been challenged to continue my work,
which in turn offers me the gift of learning.

Marion Wright an inspiring woman who has
believed in me from the first day we met.....
She is a gift of love and strength.
She gives of herself to many. She
makes me wonder how she does it all.

I am thankful for my long-time friends,
Deirdre and Holly, who have been by my side
during my own losses.

And, to people who were there along the way: Cec Smale, a gentle "man" who trusted me to help his people; Pauline Petek, for supporting me to keep moving forward no matter what. I am ever thankful to my mentor, Ralph Perry.

I am grateful to Leona Wilson for planting the seed, by suggesting the need for a book that will help professionals know how to guide their people through life interrupting events.

To Bob La Riviere, for his genuine giving of his heart and guidance when proofing my materials and to Sheryl Lubbock for her dedicated and compassionate commitment to make this book what it needed to be.

I would like to thank Roslyn and Glenn Crichton, co-founders of COPING (Caring of People in Grief), who were my support guides when my mother died. They were also instrumental in my professional development, by exposing me to a career in supporting people through loss.

My family, Howard (father), Mother (Lucy), Brother Carl, Sisters Shirley and Sharon and their families. Thank you for believing in me.

I thank my husband who has made my dream come true by supporting and encouraging me not to give up on my dream, and by helping to keep my sanity through my own losses. Thank you Claude, I love you.

Last but not least, I thank the spiritual side of my life for keeping me on track when things got complicated. Thank you God.

My Mission in Life . . .

To help others prepare for and come to terms with their traumatic experiences is my life-long commitment. To listen, feel and help with my heart.

As a Certified Trauma Specialist, Master Trainer (ASIST) and Bereavement Companion, it has been my pleasure to speak to, train and help individuals, corporations and not for profit community groups around the world.

My approach to crisis education is both proactive and reactive. Proactively, I provide the skills and tools people need to live through a crisis. On the reactive side, I have spent thousands of hours companioning people in many crisis situations and teaching frontline, management, human resources and more about how to talk and support each other for the many days ahead after a crisis situation.

It's been my privilege to companion people with loss such as their health and death of a loved one. I have been instrumental in assisting survivors of disasters such as the Oklahoma City Bombing, Ice Storm '98, Walkerton Crisis, the Manitoba Floods, and the Sept. 11th terrorist attacks on New York.

As an extension of their Human Resources, Risk Management, and Health & Safety departments, I have helped individuals and organizations come to terms with accidents, murder, suicide, death, illness, and natural perils.

Sincerely,

Laurie Martin

About the author – Laurie M. Martin

One of only a handful of Certified Trauma Specialists (CTS) in Canada, Laurie is an innovator with an impressive background and a welcoming style. Through her company, *Life Interrupted Incorporated*, she offers customized keynotes, workshops, training programs and coaching. She also designs organizational plans for corporations and community groups.

When it comes to helping others learn about loss, stress and trauma, Laurie draws from personal experience. Her warmth, sensitive humour, and sincerity elevate her training and awareness programs to a uniquely personal level. Laurie is recognized for her expertise and "People Preparedness" curriculum that includes Grief/Crisis, Suicide Intervention Training, Robbery Trauma, Workplace Violence, Crisis Intervention, Team Development and a series of wellness programs including stress and family balance. Laurie believes that a true leader is one of heart, soul and mind.

Following the Oklahoma City Bombing, Laurie co-ordinated and assisted a team of interventionists. She was an integral part of the National Hurricane Disaster Committee, providing trauma education for Emergency Responders for the Cayman Island Government. She co-ordinated the intervention for the Manitoba Canada Floods, provided grief education support in the Walkerton Crisis, presented information to organizations in the U.S. and Canada following the September 11th U.S. terrorist attacks, and was also invited to support the people of Grenada, following the recent hurricane that devastated the Caribbean Islands.

Laurie has shared her expertise on Toronto One T.V., Canada A.M., the Andy Barrie Show, Entrepreneurs (CJOB Radio), A.M. 740, and MIX 106. She has been featured in the Municipality World, Canadian Insurance Magazine, Ontario Health & Safety Magazine, HR Professional, Canadian HR Reporter, EAP Digest, RCMP Gazette, and various syndicated news publications internationally.

Transforming individuals, corporate spirit and teams! Life Interrupted Incorporated sessions are customized to meet your unique and specific needs!

LIFE INTERRUPTED
INCORPORATED

Keynote Speaking • Training • Coaching